CARTOONING
AIDS
AROUND THE
WORLD

To Judy —
Good Health

Maury Forman

KENDALL/HUNT PUBLISHING COMPANY
2460 Kerper Boulevard P.O. Box 539 Dubuque, Iowa 52004-0539

CHARLES GRIFFIN
The Daily Mirror, London
UNITED KINGDOM

CARTOONING AIDS AROUND THE WORLD

Edited by
DR. MAURY FORMAN & DAVID HORSEY

Foreword by
CONGRESSMAN JIM McDERMOTT

Contributors
JERRY ROBINSON & JENS ROBINSON

A production of

 and **cartoonists & writers syndicate**

CONTENTS

ROAR HAGEN
Oslo
NORWAY

1

FOREWORD

By JIM McDERMOTT, M.D.
Member of Congress

During my travel to many parts of the world to observe the AIDS epidemic in its multiple cultural manifestations, I have witnessed a common evolution of awareness of this disease. First, nations deny its existence. Then, they admit the disease exists but insist it afflicts only others. Finally dawns the cruel realization that AIDS has no favorites among us and scare tactics give way to meaningful educational efforts.

The shared grief of AIDS connects people in every corner of the world. But it is not our only common bond. Humor may reveal to us, in a way nothing else quite can, our shared humanity — our darkest anxieties and our finest courage.

Ironically, the ability to laugh in the face of this epidemic is a critical step toward confronting and overcoming it. For as long as a society cannot laugh in the face of calamity, it cannot relax enough to acknowledge its existence and to address it in a straightforward way.

This book suggests that the world is beginning to laugh, and so, there is hope.

ACKNOWLEDGEMENTS

This book was developed to educate people about AIDS as an international problem. The United Nations World Health Organization has recorded almost 500,000 AIDS cases worldwide, yet it is suspected that some countries have underreported the actual number of cases by 90 percent. The problem is huge. Because it may be some time before a cure is found, an immediate need for AIDS patients everywhere is help with support services that allow them to function while coping with the disease.

Proceeds from this book will go to support such organizations worldwide. Notable among these groups is the Chicken Soup Brigade, an all volunteer support network for people with AIDS. It was one of the first volunteer programs in the USA to respond to the AIDS crisis by specifically focusing on the practical needs of those disabled by AIDS. The Brigade is directed by the skillful and caring Carol Sterling whose dedication and love for the program and those associated with it knows no bounds.

There are three people who have influenced the production of this book and it is with deep regret that they were not able to live to see the book published: Robert O'Boyle, columnist for the *Seattle Times*, whose words brought home the reality of living with AIDS; Michael Harmon, whose cartoons about AIDS consistently combined humor with sadness; and Bill Jetland whose good nature and optimism never let the disease ruin his zest for living.

There have been numerous people who have assisted this project. Space does not allow us to mention in detail the important role each of them played, but our sincere appreciation goes to Jim Rosengren, Jim Murray, Len Hilgerman, Mike Williams, Mary Petus, Jennifer Savage, Richard West, Elizabeth Robinson, Bill Helfand, Pam Sparr and the ever-patient Mariel Damaskin. Special thanks go to the *Seattle Post-Intelligencer* for logistical support and to Duane Hoffmann and Kim Carney of the *Post-Intelligencer's* art department for assistance in this book's design and assembly.

Finally, we want to express our gratitude to the 61 political cartoonists who so generously donated their work to this book. May their art always flourish and keep us alert to new perils.

INTRODUCTION:
Cartoonists and the New Plague

By DAVID HORSEY and DR. MAURY FORMAN

What's so funny about AIDS? Not a thing. That is why cartoons about the disease are so important.

Aquired Immune Deficiency Syndrome scares people. It makes them deny such a horrible thing can happen to them. It makes them want to ignore the need to pay for research to find a cure. It makes them want to isolate people who have it. It makes them want to treat AIDS victims with less compassion and judge them as less moral than those who have avoided infection.

But satire is subversive. A good cartoon can tunnel under the walls of fear. Laughter can pry open a closed mind. Graphic satire can embarass people into caring and, perhaps, give a moment of comfort to a victim.

If nothing else, political cartoons, such as those that comprise this book, point a finger at a problem many would just as soon forget. They say, "Pay attention! This is a matter of life and death!"

For centuries, artists have portrayed the impact of diseases on their societies. During the 14th Century, when plague claimed the lives of half the people of Europe, paintings, etchings and frescoes were filled with pictures of the dead and dying and skeletal figures with scythes harvesting a woeful humanity. End-of-the-world images were common, redolent with stark allusions to the fourth horseman of the apocalypse: "And Behold a pale horse, and he that sat upon him his name was Death..." (Rev. 6:8).

With the development of political cartoons in the 18th and early 19th centuries, artists moved beyond mere portrayals of sickness and mortality. The cartoonists established the role that continues for them today: giving warning and placing blame. Following the influenza epidemic of 1803, for instance, English caricaturist James West produced an etching that pictured a delegation of doctors who had profited from the epidemic giving profuse thanks to "the Right Honorable Mr. Influenzy for his kind visit to this country." By the end of the 19th Century, with the political cartooning profession firmly established, caricaturists were raising alarms about each new spread of disease and decrying the unhealthy conditions in the tenements of the poor that fostered the spread of sickness.

In 1903, cartoons in Seattle and San Francisco warned of the bubonic plague epidemic. Illustrations showing how rats spread the disease informed people of the importance of cleanliness. A famous editorial cartoon entitled "moving Day for Rats" showed the ugly vermin packing their bags and leaving the city of Seattle. Cartoons also taught communities how to pull together in times of epidemics. Front page editorial cartoons alerted people about avoiding scarlet fever. Cartoons which showed housewives cleaning up refuse, inspecting children and teaching youngsters not to play together were credited with limiting the epidemic to only a few months duration in some regions. During the worldwide influenza pandemic of 1918-19, newspapers again turned to cartoonists to inform readers of the peril.

In Europe, during the First World War and on into the 1920s and '30s, it was poster artists who raised alarms about disease. French artists appealed to the soldiers of their country to avoid the "seductions of the street" that would lead to venereal disease and "useless death without honor." Artists from several countries produced riveting poster images warning about tuberculosis and educating the public about ways to prevent the disease.

Back in the U.S. in the 1950s, Daniel Fitzpatrick's bold, smog-laden cartoons helped get the air cleaned up in St. Louis before catastrophic illnesses reached the population. His cartoons were intended to elicit a response from the public and those in authority by overstating and overheating the issue. It is in just this way that political cartoonists in all times seek to become catalysts for action.

Cartoonists have been on vigilant duty at their drawing boards whenever a potential epidemic needed to be brought to the attention of the public. Whatever the scourge — bubonic plague, smallpox, scarlet fever, diptheria, tuberculosis, influenza, venereal disease — it has been, and still is, the cartoonist's duty to act as a watchdog; or as Walt Kelly, creator of "Pogo," once said, "to growl warnings, to bark, to surmise that every strange footfall is that of a cat, to worry about birds and to suspect unknown insects."

And so it has been with AIDS. For a decade, cartoonists have delivered warnings to the public and policymakers. Historians will look at cartoons drawn in the 1980s and '90s and see how this epidemic grew, how it changed lives and how the people of the world struggled with moral, political and ethical issues as they tried to face up to this new terror.

AIDS was not even identified as a distinct disease until 1981, though the viruses that cause it have existed for decades, if not centuries, according to Dr. Mirko Grmek, a historian and physician at the Sorbonne in Paris. The disease was apparently concealed by the more easily identifiable killer infections of the past and contained by conservative sexual practices and limited use of blood transfusions. But, by the time five homosexual men with a mysterious malady came to the attention of a Hollywood doctor, Michael Gottlieb, in 1980 and early '81, medical science and social mores had changed. New discoveries and techniques in virology and immunology suddenly made the disease identifiable. And a revolution in sexual behavior opened a path for widespread transmission of the virus.

Fairly quickly, AIDS entered the awareness of the general public. By 1985, when one of Dr. Gottlieb's movie star patients, Rock Hudson, died from the disease, AIDS was front-page news. But, since it seemed to be a disease of those at the margins of world society — immigrants, intravenous drug users, gay men, prostitutes, hapless Third World populations — those living in the mainstream felt safe and smug. For some, who looked at the list of victims and saw only fornicators and sodomites, AIDS appeared to be nothing less than the just wrath of an angry God.

In some countries, where AIDS had not spread, nationality was assumed to provide safety. In Japan, for instance, the name for AIDS was "the foreigners' disease." As late as 1987, the only identified Japanese AIDS victims were hemophiliacs who had contracted the disease from tainted blood imported from the United States. No one talked about the likelihood the virus would be picked up and brought home by Japanese businessmen on "sex tours" through the brothels of Southeast Asia.

In the Soviet Union, years of neglect and corruption had so undermined the medical system that the primary means of AIDS transmission was through dirty government needles and the tainted public blood supply. Yet little was done to remedy the situation.

In Africa, the disease spread at a rate unequaled anywhere else in the world. In some major cities, such as Lusaka, Zambia and Kampala, Uganda, as many as 20 percent of the adult population was infected. By the start of the 1990s, 40 percent of newborns in Zimbabwe came into the world with the virus. Yet, for years, many African governments minimized the crisis, perhaps because they knew they hadn't the resources to cope with it.

The policies of the U.S. government were contorted by raging debates about the extent of the problem, the necessity of a government-led response and the moral aspects of the issue. At first slow to react, the Reagan administration and, subsequently, the Bush administration, eventually poured millions of dollars into research. But AIDS activists insisted much more money was needed and accused the national government of dragging its feet. Countering that argument were those who said AIDS programs were already getting far more funding than efforts directed at less politically-charged diseases, such as breast cancer, which claimed more lives. In between were medical researchers who cautioned that no amount of money was guaranteed to buy a quick fix. Dr. William Haseltine, chief of human retrovirology at Boston's Dana Farber Institute, told the Associated Press, "We are making slow, steady, spectacular progress, but if society wants a quick answer from us, they are not going to get it. The immediate solution to this is very low-tech: Stop having unsafe sex with people you don't know."

That was a safeguard on which all sides agreed. But, to some, safe sex meant condoms and less anal intercourse. To others it meant abstinence outside of marriage and a rejection of non-monogamous, non-marital, non-heterosexual lovemaking. While AIDS activists warned that everyone was at risk, conservatives insisted that people with conventional lifestyles had little to worry about.

Meanwhile, though it was obvious some groups were more at risk than others, as the second decade of AIDS began, it was clear the disease in America could no longer be branded a "gay men's disease" (which it never was in other parts of the world). Heterosexual transmission was becoming more common and there were fears of widespread outbreaks on college campuses where sexual license was seldom tempered with the caution required for safe sex.

Globally, the biggest worry was the spread of AIDS to Asia and an intensifying level of infection in Africa. The World Health Organization was predicting the virus might strike 40 million people by the year 2000. Ninety percent of those afflicted would be citizens of developing countries. There were still countries which seemed safe. In Turkey, for instance, only 60 cases of AIDS infection had been found by 1992, according to officials of the Turkish health ministry. Turkish doctors expressed confidence that the more prim sexual practices of their Islamic society would keep them immune. Others, though, were becoming less sanguine about the prospects for the spread of the disease to new regions of the world. At the international AIDS conference in Florence, Italy in 1991, Vulimiri Ramalingaswami of the All India Institute of Medical Science in New Delhi said there was no longer any hope that Asia would escape the curse of AIDS.

"The Asian drama of AIDS is unfolding," he said. "In the developing coutries we are sitting on top of a volcano. I am here to plead for a human and global response to a developing disaster."

The response of political cartoonists to the rise of AIDS parallels, in many ways, the response of the general public. This is not surprising because, while cartoonists document and lampoon the thoughts, fears and biases of their societies, they also cannot avoid being affected by them. Much as they may like to think so, cartoonists are not entirely a breed apart from the common man and woman.

Cartoons done on the subject prior to 1985 are scarce. An annual collection of North American graphic political satire,

"Best Editorial Cartoons of the Year," did not feature a single cartoon about AIDS until 1988, even though those volumes usually feature a section dealing with health issues and are composed of work submitted by a broad cross-section of working cartoonists. Up to that point, apparently, few, if any, U.S. or Canadian editorial cartoonists ranked drawings about AIDS among their most important work.

When we sent out our call for submissions to this book, we heard back from several very accomplished practitioners of the art who confessed they had not yet dealt with AIDS in their work. Irish cartoonist Martyn Turner wrote, "Truth is, as sex is all but illegal in Ireland and we pretend people use needles for nothing more illicit than shoving hormones into cows, I've never done a cartoon on the subject of AIDS."

On the other hand, we found a number of cartoonists who had repeatedly joined in the hot debate generated by the AIDS crisis. Of particular note among North American artists are Joel Pett of *The Lexington Herald Leader*, Jimmy Margulies formerly of *The Houston Post*, (now of *The Record* in Hackensack, N.J.), Mike Keefe of *The Denver Post*, Aislin of *The Montreal Gazette*, Tony Auth of *The*

Philadelphia Inquirer, Jim Borgman of *The Cincinnatti Enquirer*, Dan Wasserman of *The Boston Globe* and Garry Trudeau, creator of "Doonesbury." And this is the short list.

A deadly disease is not a simple issue for a cartoonist to deal with. First, and most obviously, humor, the cartoonist's number-one tool, is not easily employed. Sometimes nothing more than an ironic grimace is appropriate. But, since the central purpose of political cartooning is to make people think, not just to make them laugh, this handicap is minor. More difficult is knowing just what to say. AIDS is evil. Death is sad. Disease is horrible. Such truisms can be stated only so many ways without becoming trite and clichéd. The cartoonists have found their way past this pitfall by diving into the swirl of issues that orbit around the central, grim reality of the disease; medical questions, political chicanery, social phobias and lifestyle reassessments.

Our method of assembling this collection of cartoons should be noted. We sent out a general call to a broad selection of North American political cartoonists asking them to send us copies of their best work on AIDS and related subjects. From these initial submissions, we made a rough cut and then filled gaps by telephoning additional artists who had failed to respond to our first invitation. We used this same method to reach some of the artists outside of North America. But, for the bulk of the non-U.S. cartoons, we relied on Jerry Robinson whose Cartoonists and Writers Syndicate markets the work of a long list of international cartoonists. We make no claim that this book represents an exhaustive survey of AIDS cartoons done by the world's graphic satirists. These are just some of them, taken from the mainstream press of a limited number of countries. But we can say, with assurance, they are some of the very best. Among the 61 artists from 21 countries are 6 Pulitizer prize winners and many more who are deserving of awards.

 The AIDS epidemic will not be easily conquered. Many millions of human beings are bound to die before the disease is controlled or eradicated. But, as we live through this fearful time, our travail will be lessened if bigotry, stupidity and political timidity can be replaced by compassion, wisdom and commitment. It is in that effort that the world's political cartoonists will be our unfailing allies.

YURI IVANOV
Moscow
RUSSIA

IVANOV

HISTORICAL PERSPECTIVE:
International Political Art

By JERRY ROBINSON and JENS ROBINSON

Society's response to the threat of AIDS is dramatically illustrated by the work of concerned artists worldwide. In addition to 29 cartoonists from the United States, 32 cartoonists from 20 other countries are represented in this unique collection. They speak eloquently and with powerful imagery. Kambiz (Switzerland) employs a satiric version of the frog and princess fable. Sinchinov (Russia) imaginatively transforms the letter "S" in AIDS into a dollar-shaped serpent. Reisinger (Croatia) depicts a death figure and a blinded earth. KAL (England) depicts the four horsemen of the apocalypse being joined by a dread newcomer — AIDS.

There are discernable stylistic differences between the foreign cartoon and its counterpart in the United States. Without the restrictions of format required by syndication in the American press, cartoons from abroad, in general, depend less on captions and dialogue, relying to a greater degree on pure graphics to convey the message. Moreover, for a variety of historical reasons, cartoons from countries outside the Anglo-American tradition generally treat their subject matter more symbolically and are less issue-specific than those from the United Kingdom, Oceania and North America.

Beginning in the 16th century, numerous European artists, most notably Goya, took up graphic journalism in the form of prints and broadsheets. The 19th century brought the penetrating chroniclers of English society — William Hogarth, James Gilray and Thomas Rowlandson. Hogarth was described by David Low as "the first to infuse a characteristically English spirit into this practice of the art and thus found an English school distinct from other schools in the [European] continent." Their biting satire centered on the plagues of that day — poverty, disease, graft, greed and alcoholism.

With the establishment of the magazines *La Caricature* (1830) and *Le Charivari* (1832), Paris supplanted London, for a time, as the vibrant center for political and social satire. Henri Daumier drew a devastating series of drawings on the French monarchy including one savaging King Louis Philippe as Gargantua gorging himself on the working class. Daumier's editor, Charles Philipon, metamorphosed the royal visage into a pear. The drawings sent both to jail — proving that the political cartoon is not only a powerful instrument in marshalling public opinion, but also a dangerous profession for the practitioner.

The satiric journal medium was spreading. In England, *Punch* (1841), originally subtitled, *The London Charivari*, featured the art of John Leech and John Tenniel. *Le Rire* (1894) was published in Paris with cartoons by Toulouse Lautrec, and in the same year, *Yellow Book* was published in London with the work of Max Beerbohm and Aubrey Beardsley. The tradition traveled overseas with the establishment of the *Melbourne Punch* (1855) and the *Bulletin* (1880) in Australia. In North America, *Punch* in Canada was followed by *Leslie's Illustrated Weekly* (1855), *Harper's Weekly* (1857) and *Puck* (1877).

In the next half-century, national satiric journals emerged in other countries, including: *Simplissimus* (1896), Germany: *Krokodil* (1922), USSR; *Spilki* (1935), Poland; and after the Second World War, *Hosteni* (1945), Albania, and *Osten* (1947), Yugoslavia. Others representative of the genre in Europe were: *Ludas Matyi*, Hungary; *Tururut*, Spain; *Karikaturk*, Turkey; and *Jez*, Yugoslavia.

Satiric journals also achieved popularity in Latin America: *Pasquim* and *Humor*, Argentina; *Rayas,* Mexico; and *La Semana Comica*, Nicaragua. The Australian school included artists Phil May and Norman Lindsay; in Poland, Eryk Lipinski and Szymon Kobylinski; and in the USSR, Kukriniksi, the pen name for the unique collection of three enormously talented Russian artists,

Kuprianov, Krilov and Sokolov. The influence of western political/social satire is seen at the turn of the century in the work of Japan's greatest cartoonist, Kitazawa and later, Ryuichi Yokoyama.

In the latter half of the 19th century, contemporaneously with the nurturing of political/social satire in journals, there was a growing convention of political cartoons in the daily press, and it soon became a fixture in major newspapers throughout the world. Thereafter, newspapers became the most important vehicle in the development of the political cartoon.

Times of crisis are shots of adrenaline to cartoonists. For Daumier, it was the horror of war; for Hogarth, the drugs and disease of urban slums. The art of the great *Simplissimus* cartoonists, George Grosz, Heinrich Kley and Olaf Gulbransson focused on greed, sex and religion. These artists/activists were the precursors of David Low, whose brilliant cartoons helped to alert a complacent world to the rise of fascism. In our own day, the tradition is carried on by cartoonists such as the Netherlands' Behrendt, Sweden's Ewk, Norway's Hagen, Israel's Kirschen, Canada's

Raeside, France's Tim and Plantu along with their colleagues whose work is seen in this collection. These cartoonists believe it is their moral imperative to fight the scourge of our generation, AIDS, the way they know best — with pen and ink.

Cultural and political repression in much of the world in the 17th to 19th centuries dictated extensive use of historical, biblical and mythological allegory. In the 20th century, poster-like images were frequently employed to make political statements. Cartoonists had to master the art of subtlety; their political/social views were often hidden in design or symbolism.

Twentieth century totalitarianism has made its own mark on political cartooning — from Latin American dictatorships to the Chinese Cultural Revolution. Indeed, forms of propaganda using cartoons are universal, but undemocratic regimes have made words and pictures into an instrument of the state. An exhibition of anti-imperialist caricatures from 24 countries opened in Beijing in 1966-67. It extolled Mao and employed stereotypes of Uncle Sam and bloated capitalists raping Vietnam at the same time China was suppressing freedom of expression by its own artists.

Cartoonists suffered a not too different fate in the former Soviet Union, where dissent put critics of the state, such as Viatcheslav Syssoyev, in the gulag. Francisco Laurenzo Pons was jailed and tortured by the military junta in Uruguay for his political cartoons. Others fled their country, such as Ardeshir Mohassess, who was forced to leave Iran for his opposition to the Shah and later, ironically, prevented from returning because of his unwillingness to bend to the Ayatollah.

Beginning with Gorbachev's policy of glasnost, there has been a new vitality in the arts of the former Eastern bloc regimes. Many of these countries' finest artists, previously unable to have their work published, are now producing striking graphics and a wide diversity of styles. What they do have in common is a passion born of years of repression. Despite certain universalities, the discussion of AIDS is distinctly a part of each nation's own culture. A vivid example is Magic Johnson's revelation that he is HIV positive. In the United States, where Magic is a revered sports hero, his story received extensive media coverage, creating a level of AIDS awareness few others could have achieved. As seen in the cartoons from abroad in this collection, however, other perspectives on the AIDS issue predominate.

These powerful images by the world's concerned cartoonists comprise a priceless contribution in the fight to combat AIDS, the evil fifth horse of the apocalypse.

THIS BOOK IS DEDICATED TO THE ONES WE LOVE:

Mary, Joshua and Adam

Nole Ann, Darielle and Daniel

THE NEW PLAGUE

We begin with images depicting the awesome evil of AIDS with a broad and brutal brush. Here, cartoonists have tried to capture the immensity of the problem in stark, often simple, images. The predominance of skeletal death figures in black robes recalls the work of the death-obsessed 14th Century artists of Europe who sought to portray the plague of their time. For today's artists, humor shrivels in the shadow of the new peril.

JOEL PETT
Lexington Herald Leader
USA

JIM BORGMAN
Cincinnati Enquirer
USA

15

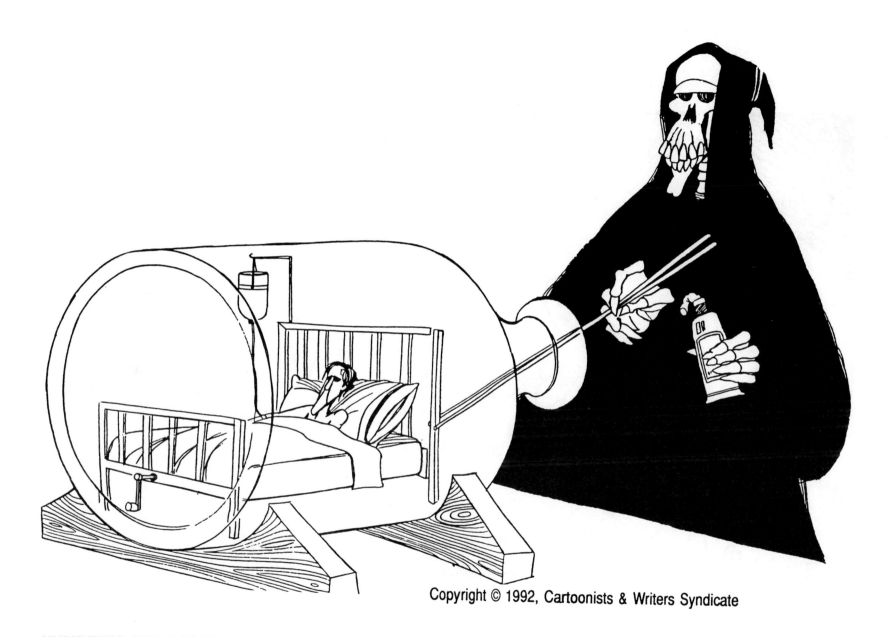

HUMBERTO DE LA TORRE
YA, Madrid
SPAIN

16

DOUGLAS DOUMONT
El Tiempo, San Pedro Sula
HONDURAS

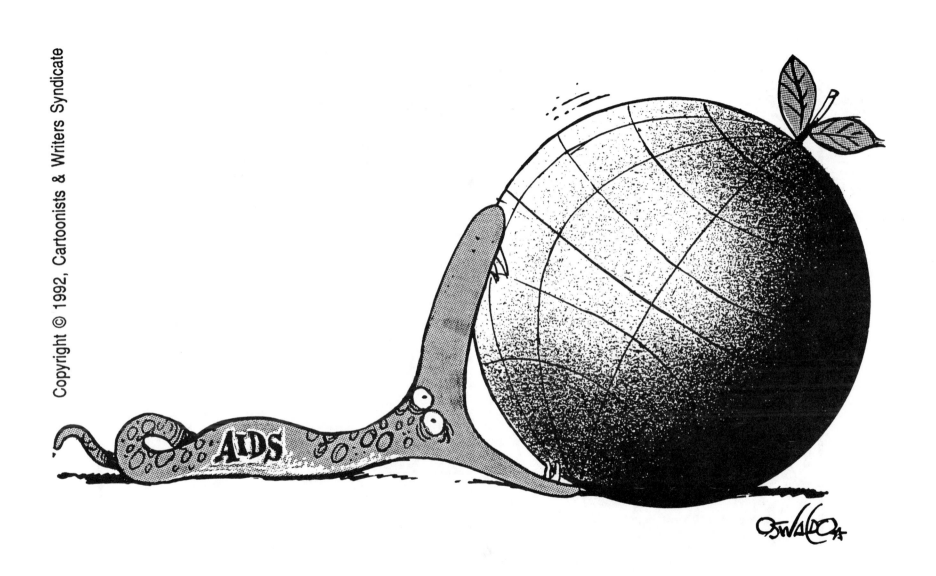

OSWALDO SAGASTEGUI
Excelsior, Mexico City
MEXICO

18

KAL (KEVIN KALLAUGHER)
Sunday Telegraph, London
UNITED KINGDOM

JUAN BALLESTA
Madrid
SPAIN

"BLOCK ANTAGONISM?... NUCLEAR WEAPON?... REGIONAL WARS?...
TERRORISM?... POLLUTION?... AIDS?..."

OTO REISINGER
Zagreb
CROATIA

20

EYITAYO FATUNLA
This Week, Lagos
NIGERIA

BAS MITROPOULOS
Athens
GREECE

22

ROWI (ROBERTO WILLIAMS)
La Prensa, San Pedro Sula
HONDURAS

23

JOEL PETT
Lexington Herald Leader
USA

LOVE ON THE ROCKS

Cartoonists have found a rich vein of material to be mined in the various ways lifestyles have been altered in response to the new reality of AIDS. In the eyes of the artists, dating has become an exercise in caution, lovemaking seems fraught with peril and sex via telephone seems a rational option. The sexual revolution may not have ground to a halt, but it seems to have taken on the characteristics of a guerrilla war.

BILL MITCHELL
The Australian, Sydney
AUSTRALIA

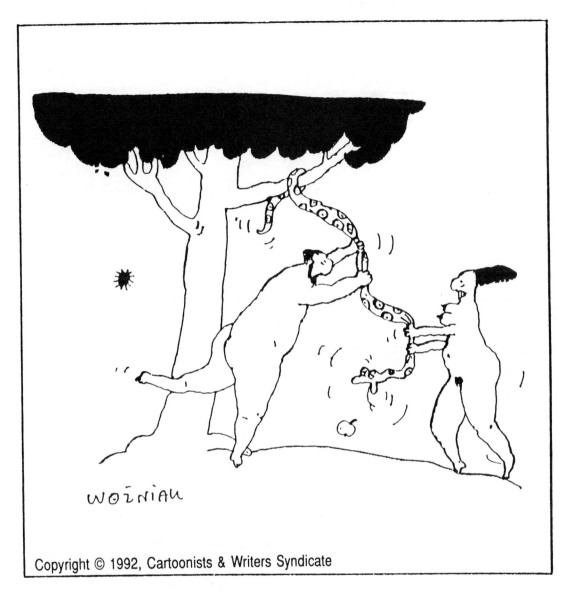

"AIDS won't get me!"

JACEK WOZNIAK
Le Canard Enchaine, Paris
FRANCE

DAVID HORSEY
The Seattle Post-Intelligencer
USA

JEAN PLANTU
Le Monde, Paris
FRANCE

29

Copyright © 1992, Cartoonists & Writers Syndicate

EWK (EWERT KARLSSON)
Aftonbladet, Stockholm
SWEDEN

STEVE BELL
The Guardian, London
UNITED KINGDOM

ROB ROGERS
The Pittsburgh Press
USA

NORMAN ISAAC
Bulletin Today, Manila
PHILIPPINES

JOEL PETT
Lexington Herald Leader
USA

34

ANDY DONATO
The Toronto Sun
CANADA

35

JACK OHMAN
The Oregonian, Portland
USA

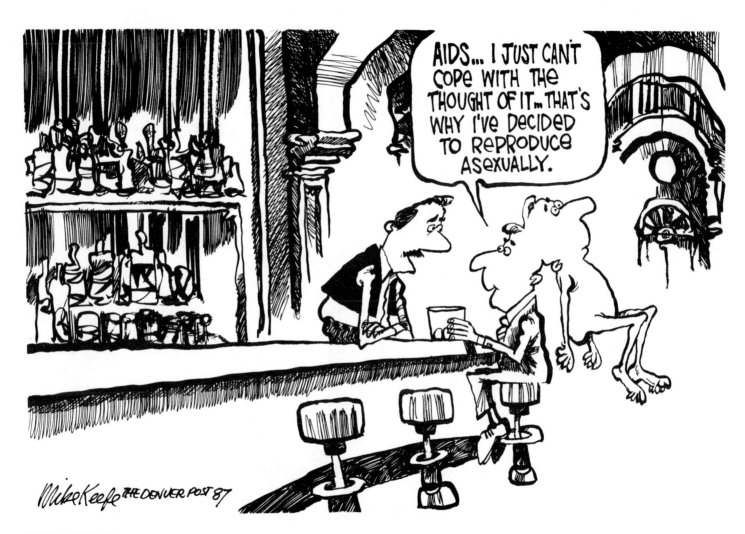

MIKE KEEFE
The Denver Post
USA

SIGNE WILKINSON
Philadelphia Daily News
USA

DAVID HORSEY
The Seattle Post-Intelligencer
USA

39

KAMBIZ DERAMBAKHSH
Nebelspalter, Basel
SWITZERLAND

AISLIN (TERRY MOSHER)
The Gazette, Montreal
CANADA

CLUB MED AND AIDS

"Henceforth, the currency of exchange will be the condom."

CABU (JEAN CABUT)
Le Canard Enchaine, Paris
FRANCE

CHAPERONE

MILT PRIGGEE
The Spokesman Review/Spokane Chronicle
USA

CHRIS BRITT
The Morning News-Tribune, Tacoma
USA

THE NEW SEXUAL REVOLUTION

STEVE GREENBERG
The Seattle Post-Intelligencer
USA

Dry Bones

 THANKS TO THE AIDS PLAGUE..

 THE **ONE** NAME THAT...

WILL **NOT** BE GIVEN TO...

 THE LAST DECADE

 OF THE TWENTIETH CENTURY

 IS "THE GAY NINETY'S"

YA'AKOV KIRSCHEN
The Jerusalem Post
ISRAEL

FORGET IT, BUDDY!! TONIGHT, TWO NEGATIVES WILL NOT BE MAKING A POSITIVE...

I tested NEGATIVE for AIDS

I tested NEGATIVE for AIDS

AISLIN (TERRY MOSHER)
The Gazette, Montreal
CANADA

"HEY, WHATTAYOU CRAZY?! YOU CAN SPREAD AIDS WITH THESE THINGS!"

JIM BORGMAN
Cincinnati Enquirer
USA

47

SIGNE WILKINSON
Philadelphia Daily News
USA

48

PAT OLIPHANT
Washington
USA

JIM BORGMAN
Cincinnati Enquirer
USA

50

FEARING FEAR ITSELF

Any epidemic raises fears. But, because of the baffling nature of AIDS, because it can be transmitted through the most intimate of human acts and because of the predominance of victims among scorned sectors of society, most of the fears and phobias generated by the disease have gone far beyond prudence to escape all bounds of rationality. Heartless insurance executives, anti-gay mobs, cruel school children and other worried and worrisome types populate the cartoons in the following pages.

TONY AUTH

The Philadelphia Inquirer

USA

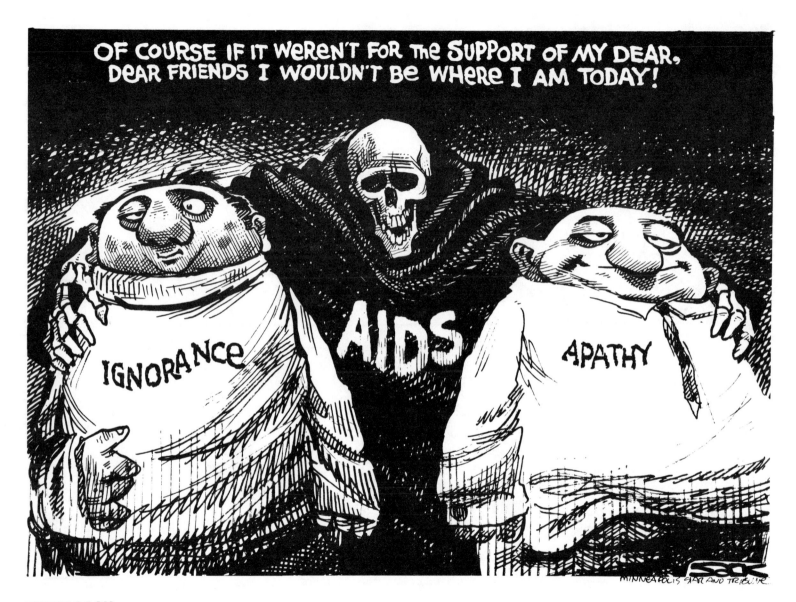

STEVE SACK

Star Tribune, Minneapolis

USA

TOM TOLES
The Buffalo News
USA

EFBE (FRANS DE BOER)
Amsterdam
NETHERLANDS

WALTER HANEL
Frankfurter Allegemeine, Bonn
GERMANY

56

JOEL PETT
Lexington Herald Leader
USA

TOM TOLES
The Buffalo News
USA

EUGENIE SINCHINOV
Moscow
RUSSIA

JOEL PETT
Lexington Herald Leader
USA

JIMMY MARGULIES
Houston Post
USA

DAN WASSERMAN
The Boston Globe
USA

TONY AUTH
The Philadelphia Inquirer
USA

JOEL PETT
Lexington Herald Leader
USA

MIKE KEEFE
The Denver Post
USA

TOM TOLES
The Buffalo News
USA

THE SCARLET LETTER

MIKE KEEFE
The Denver Post
USA

J.D. CROWE
The Tribune, San Diego
USA

BILL DEORE
The Dallas Morning News
USA

GARRICK TREMAIN
Otago Daily Times, Queenstown
NEW ZEALAND

Q. Which disease is spread by casual contact?

A. Feared virus

B. Virulent fear

DAN WASSERMAN
The Boston Globe
USA

A PLACE WHERE NO ONE IS AFRAID TO HUG

JIM BORGMAN
Cincinnati Enquirer
USA

AIDS POLITICS

The next set of cartoons lampoons the politicians of several countries who quiver at the mention of condoms and quail before the power of the righteous right wing. If the cartoonists are correct, it would seem many of our world leaders have a bad case of avoidance when it comes to AIDS. They would be happy if the disease would just go away and save them from tough decisions. Wouldn't we all?

MILT PRIGGEE
The Spokesman Review/Spokane Chronicle
USA

GOOD GOD!

I KNOW it's **UNUSUAL**, MARGARET, BUT THE **ADVERTISING CHAPPIES** NEEDED A **FIGURE** THAT **YOUNG PEOPLE** COULD **RELATE TO**....

...A SORT OF **SUPERHERO CHARACTER** TO REALLY **GET THE MESSAGE HOME**..

...AND **CAPTAIN CONDOM** SEEMED TO **FILL THE BILL** REMARKABLY **WELL**!!

IS IT A **BALLOON**?

IS IT A **PLASTIC BAG**?

NO...IT'S **CAPTAIN CONDOM**!

HI KIDS!!

SKREEK SKRAWK SKREEK SKRAWK

NOW, SOME OF US ARE **GAY**, SOME OF US ARE **STRAIGHT** AND SOME OF US ARE **AC/DC**— I'M GOING TO GIVE YOU A **FEW FACTS** ABOUT THE DIFFERENCE BETWEEN **SAFE SEX** AND **HIGH RISK SEX**. **FIRST FACT**: THE **ONLY SURE FORMS** OF **RISK-FREE SEX** ARE....

RISKO DISCO

.. **SOLO WANKING** AND **MUTUAL MASSAGE** WITHOUT **MASTURBATION**. OTHER FORMS RANGE FROM THE **FAIRLY SAFE** TO THE **POSITIVELY DANGEROUS**!..

CUT! TOTALLY UNACCEPTABLE!

WHAT ABOUT **MARRIAGE**?

RELIGIOUS ADVISER

MORAL PARAGON

STEVE BELL
The Guardian, London
UNITED KINGDOM

75

STEVE BELL
The Guardian, London
UNITED KINGDOM

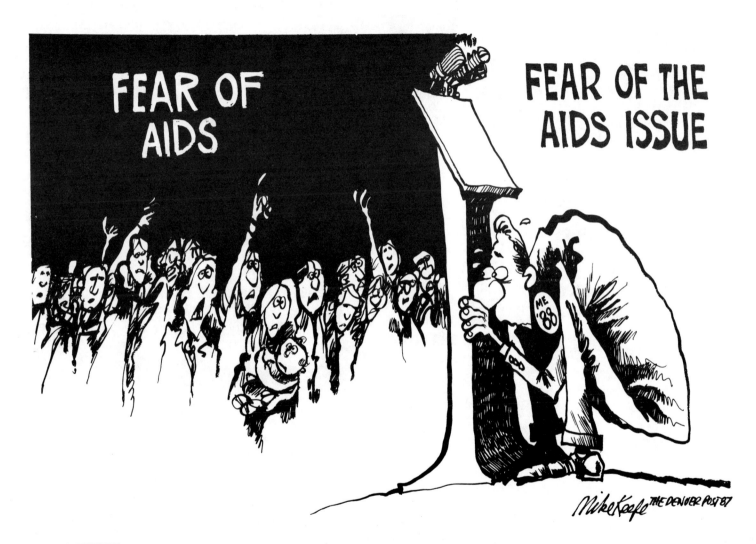

MIKE KEEFE
The Denver Post
USA

STEVE GREENBERG
The Seattle Post-Intelligencer
USA

TONY AUTH
The Philadelphia Inquirer
USA

DAN WASSERMAN
The Boston Globe
USA

RANDY WICKS
The Newhall Signal, Valencia, CA
USA

81

DAVID HORSEY
The Seattle Post-Intelligencer
USA

ETTA HULME
Fort Worth Star-Telegram
USA

BILL MITCHELL
The Australian, Sydney
AUSTRALIA

JIM MORIN
The Miami Herald
USA

85

WILEY (DAVID WILEY MILLER)
San Francisco Examiner
USA

THE MEDICAL FRONT

The war with AIDS will be won by doctors and researchers, but the quest for an AIDS remedy or drugs that might, at least, make the dying easier, has been daunting. The cartoons in this section highlight the difficulty of the process, especially the money questions: how much research money is enough? How can new drugs be made affordable? Who is getting rich in the process? Highlighted here, as well, is the controversy over AIDS testing and medical patients' frantic fears of infection.

JOHN TREVER
Albuquerque Journal
USA

KAMBIZ DERAMBAKHSH
Nebelspalter, Basel
SWITZERLAND

89

PAT OLIPHANT
Washington
USA

MIKE KEEFE
The Denver Post
USA

"AS I WAS EXPLAINING OUR RULES FOR RELEASING NEW DRUGS, HE HAD THE EFFRONTERY TO DIE!"

TIM MENEES
Pittsburgh Post-Gazette
USA

JIMMY MARGULIES
Houston Post
USA

ADRIAN RAESIDE
Times-Colonist, Victoria
CANADA

AISLIN (TERRY MOSHER)
The Gazette, Montreal
CANADA

JIMMY MARGULIES
Houston Post
USA

JOHN BRANCH
San Antonio Express-News
USA

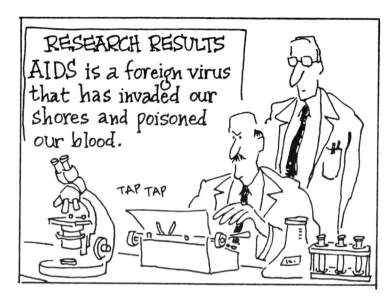

DAN WASSERMAN
The Boston Globe
USA

98

Mena

JOSE LUIS MARTIN MENA
ABC, Madrid
SPAIN

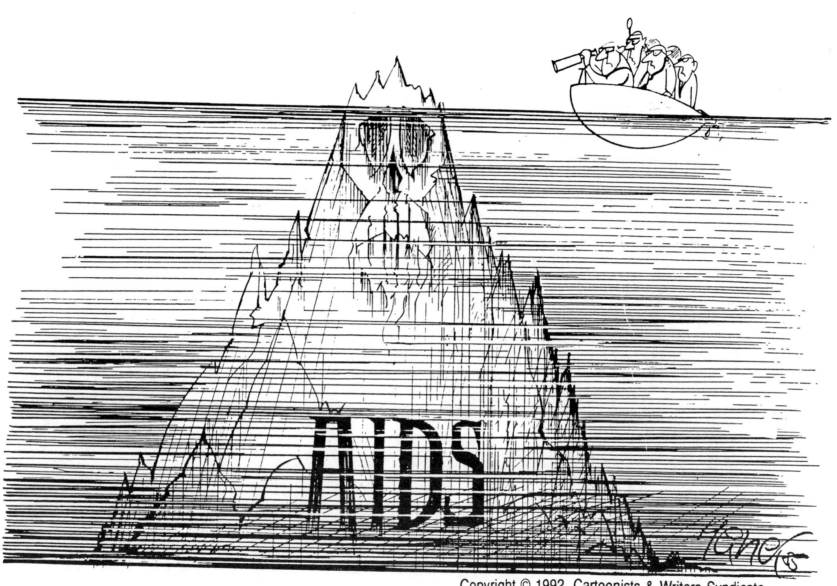

WALTER HANEL
Frankfurter Allegemeine, Bonn
GERMANY

100

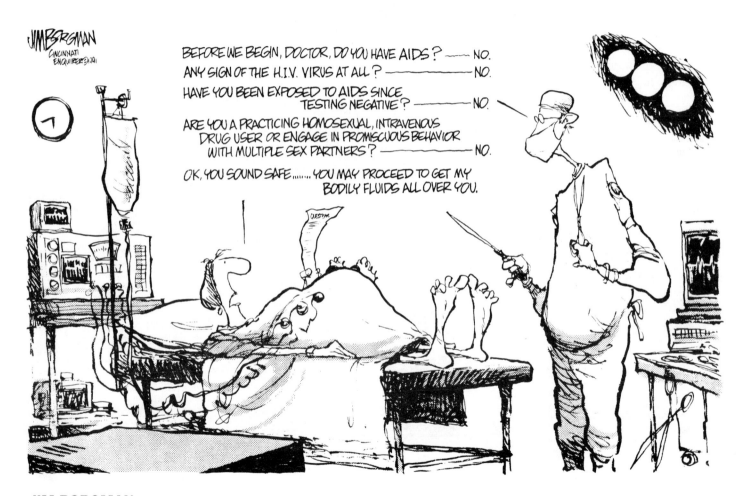

JIM BORGMAN
Cincinnati Enquirer
USA

SIGNE WILKINSON
Philadelphia Daily News
USA

IGNORANCE IS NOT BLISS

If fear and ignorance are debilitating, education would seem to be the agent for action. This final section documents the ways the world has sought to educate itself about AIDS and the ways in which such understanding is undermined. In these pages you'll find some of the many cartoons generated by American basketball star Magic Johnson's revelation that he is HIV positive. The book closes with a few selections from the comic strip "Doonesbury" which, in portraying the very personal and poignant death of one of the strip's characters, brilliantly asserted the humanity and bravery of AIDS victims.

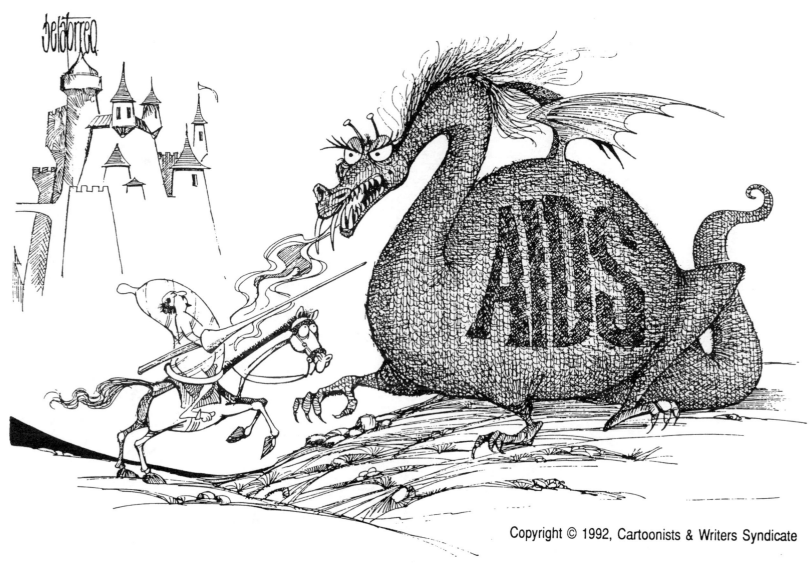

HUMBERTO DE LA TORRE
YA, Madrid
SPAIN

'...AND SO THE PRINCE AND THE PRINCESS USED CONDOMS AND HAD SAFE SEX AND LIVED HAPPILY EVER AFTER. THE END.'

PAT OLIPHANT
Washington
USA

105

DAVID HORSEY
The Seattle Post-Intelligencer
USA

JIMMY MARGULIES
Houston Post
USA

SAFER NOW?

DICK LOCHER

The Chicago Tribune
USA

108

FRITZ BEHRENDT
De Telegraaf, Amsterdam
NETHERLANDS

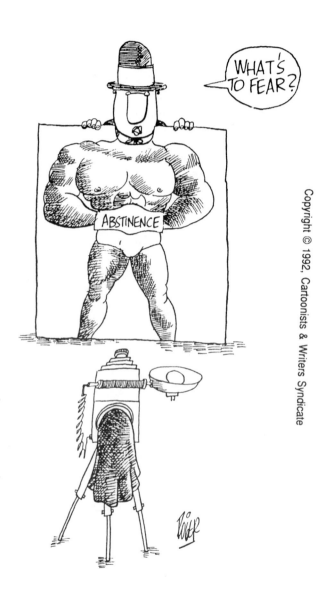

ROGER (ROGER SANCHEZ)
Managua
NICARAGUA

FRANCISCO JOSE CALDERON
El Norte, Nuevo Leon
MEXICO

MIKE LUCKOVICH
The Atlanta Constitution
USA

111

ADRIAN RAESIDE
Times-Colonist, Victoria
CANADA

JIMMY MARGULIES
Houston Post
USA

"1. TAKE OFF CLOTHES... 2. STEP INTO SHOWER... 3. TURN ON COLD WATER... 4. STAY THERE UNTIL MARRIED.... THAT'S IT?

JOHN TREVER
Albuquerque Journal
USA

'HERE I AM, EDUCATED TO DEAL WITH THE MOST INTIMATE, COMPLEX, CONTROVERSIAL SEXUAL CRISIS EVER TO FACE OUR SOCIETY—AND I'M STILL NOT SURE WHAT A "HICKEY" IS...'

STEVE SACK
Star Tribune, Minneapolis
USA

"WE HAVE A SURGE OF INTEREST HERE—CALL IT MAGIC."

TIM MENEES
Pittsburgh Post-Gazette
USA

JACK OHMAN
The Oregonian, Portland
USA

DANA SUMMERS
The Orlando Sentinel
USA

CHRIS BRITT
The Morning News-Tribune, Tacoma
USA

"WE NEED MORE THAN MAGIC ..... WE NEED MIRACLES."

JIM BORGMAN
Cincinnati Enquirer
USA

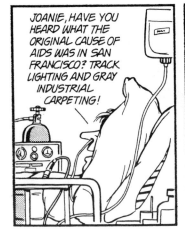

GARRY TRUDEAU
Doonesbury, New York
USA

121

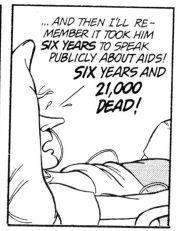

GARRY TRUDEAU
Doonesbury, New York
USA

INDEX